CW00734054

USBORNE KEY

Practice Pad

Dividing

Written by Simon Tudhope

Illustrated by Marta Cabrol

Designed by Sharon Cooper

Series Editor: Felicity Brooks

$$8 \div 2 = 4$$

At the back of this pad you'll find the answer pages, and als
some blank paper that you can use for doing calculatio

Sharing

Help Crock and Lep share out these 6 cupcakes equally onto 2 plates. Cross off each cupcake as you draw it on a plate, then complete the calculation below.

Yum, yum!

$6 \div 2 =$

each

Sharing

Help Lem and Baz share out these 10 tubs of ice cream equally into 2 baskets. Cross off each tub as you draw it in a basket, then complete the calculation below.

$$10 \div 2 = \boxed{}$$

each

Grouping

How many pairs of socks does Baz have? Draw around these 12 socks in groups of 2, then count the groups to complete the calculation below.

I should probably put those away...

$$12 \div \boxed{} = 2$$

pairs

Grouping

How many pairs of apples does Ant have? Draw around these 16 apples in groups of 2, then count the groups to complete the calculation below.

16 ÷ ⬚ = 2

pairs

Arrays

Fill in the blanks so that each array is described by both a multiplication and a division sentence.

...... x 2 = 10

...... ÷ 2 = 5

...... x 2 = 12

12 ÷ ...... = 6

3 x ...... = 6

6 ÷ ...... = 3

2 x ...... = 4

...... ÷ 2 = 2

Fact family

A fact family is a set of three numbers that can be divided or multiplied together. Fill in the blank spaces below to show the two dividing and two multiplying calculations for this fact family.

6

÷   ÷

3   2

x

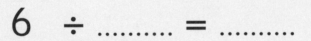

6 ÷ .... = ...

6 ÷ .... = ...

3 x .... = ...

2 x .... = ...

Fact family

Fill in the blank spaces below to show the
two dividing and two multiplying calculations
for this fact family.

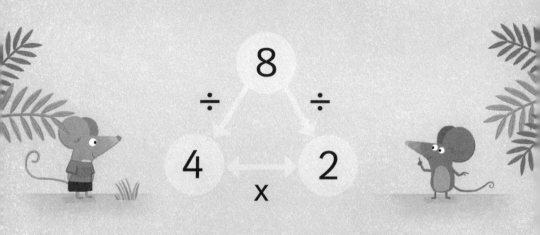

.... ÷ 4 = ...

.... ÷ .... = 4

.... x .... = 8

2 x .... = ...

Fact family

A fact family is a set of three numbers that can be divided or multiplied together. Fill in the blank spaces below to show the two dividing and two multiplying calculations for this fact family.

10

÷   ÷

5   2

x

10 ÷ .... = ...

10 ÷ .... = ...

5   x .... = ...

2   x .... = ...

Fact family

Fill in the blank spaces below to show the two dividing and two multiplying calculations for this fact family.

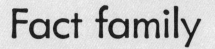

12

$\div$ $\div$

6   2

x

.... $\div$ 6   = ...

.... $\div$ .... =   6

.... x .... =   12

2   x .... = ...

Dice dots

For each row, complete the calculation to show
how many dots are on each dice.

6 dots $\div$ 3 dice $=$ 2 dots on each dice

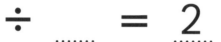

...... $\div$ ...... $=$ 2

...... $\div$ ...... $=$ 2

...... $\div$ ...... $=$ 2

Dividing by 2

These 18 tiger cubs need to be divided into 2 teams for a game in the park. Complete the calculation to show how many cubs will be in each team.

$$18 \div 2 = \boxed{}$$

Dividing by 2

Lem wants to divide 8 sports jerseys into 2 piles. Complete the calculation below to show how many jerseys will be in each pile.

$$8 \div 2 = \boxed{}$$

And how many in each pile if I divide **14** jerseys into 2 piles?

$$14 \div 2 = \boxed{}$$

2 each

A party of 16 animals has arrived at Crock's Canoe Club. Each canoe has seats for 2 animals. Complete the calculation to show how many canoes the party needs so that every animal has a seat.

$$16 \div \boxed{} = 2$$

2 each

This canoe can carry 2 passengers. Complete the calculation to find out how many trips are needed to carry 20 animals across the river.

$$20 \div \boxed{} = 2$$

And how many trips if 12 animals want to cross back again?

RIVER-CROSSING POINT

$$12 \div \boxed{} = 2$$

Calculation match-up

Help Baz find the answers to these calculations.
Draw a line to match each one with the
correct answer.

$12 \div 2$

6

10

$16 \div 2$

1

$10 \div 2$

5

4

$2 \div 2$

$6 \div 2$

$20 \div 2$

8

3

$8 \div 2$

Missing numbers

Write the missing numbers in the boxes
to complete these calculations.

$4 \div \boxed{} = 2$

$20 \div \boxed{} = 2$

$8 \div \boxed{} = 2$

$12 \div \boxed{} = 2$

$2 \div \boxed{} = 2$

$16 \div \boxed{} = 2$

Right or wrong?

Check if Tig and Tan-tan have answered these
calculations correctly. Put a ✔ or X in the boxes.
Then, turn the page.

$10 \div 2 = 4$

$12 \div 2 = 6$

$4 \div 2 = 2$

$18 \div 2 = 8$

$14 \div 2 = 5$

$6 \div 2 = 3$

$16 \div 2 = 8$

$20 \div 2 = 11$

$8 \div 2 = 4$

$0 \div 2 = 1$

$10 \div 2 = 4$

Correcting calculations

Complete the other side of this page. Then, copy the calculations that are wrong into the blank boxes below, writing the correct answers instead.

Missing numbers

Write the missing numbers in the boxes
to complete these calculations.

$$18 \div 2 = \boxed{}$$

$$\boxed{} \div 2 = 5$$

$$8 \div \boxed{} = 4$$

$$\boxed{} \div 2 = 10$$

$$16 \div \boxed{} = 8$$

$$4 \div 2 = \boxed{}$$

Number wheel

Help Cheeky complete the number wheel. Divide each number by 2 to fill in the blank spaces.

14 20

18 16

4 ÷2 6

12 10

6 8 2

Twelve divided by two is six.

÷2

Sharing

Help Crock and Lep share out these 20 oranges equally into 5 boxes. Cross off each orange as you draw it in a box, then complete the calculation below.

Boo!

$$20 \div 5 = \boxed{}$$

each

Sharing

Help Baz and Lem share out these 25 berries equally into 5 bowls. Cross off each berry as you draw it in a bowl, then complete the calculation below.

$$25 \div 5 = \boxed{}$$

each

Grouping

Help Tan-tan group these 30 bananas into 5s.
Draw around the bananas in groups of 5, then
count the groups to complete the calculation below.

$$30 \div \boxed{} = 5$$

groups

Grouping

Help Ant group these 15 pineapples into 5s. Draw around the pineapples in groups of 5, then count the groups to complete the calculation below.

$$15 \div \boxed{} = 5$$

groups

Arrays

Fill in the blanks so that each array is described by both a multiplication and a division sentence.

...... x 5 = 5

5 ÷ ...... = 1

6 x ...... = 30

30 ÷ ...... = 6

3 x ...... = 15

...... ÷ 5 = 3

...... x 5 = 45

...... ÷ 5 = 9

Fact family

A fact family is a set of three numbers that can be divided or multiplied together. Fill in the blank spaces below to show the two dividing and two multiplying calculations for this fact family.

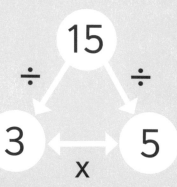

15 ÷ .... = ...

15 ÷ .... = ...

3 x .... = ...

5 x .... = ...

Fact family

Fill in the blank spaces below to show the two dividing and two multiplying calculations for this fact family.

20

÷ ÷

4 5

x

.... ÷ ...4...... = ...

.... ÷ .... = ...4......

.... x .... = ...20......

...5...... x .... = ...

Fact family

A fact family is a set of three numbers that can be divided or multiplied together. Fill in the blank spaces below to show the two dividing and two multiplying calculations for this fact family.

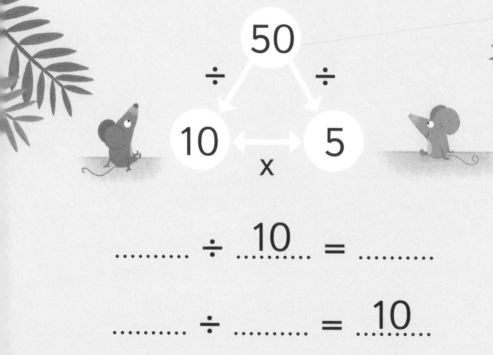

.... ÷ ..10.. = ...

.... ÷ .... = ..10..

.... x .... = ..50..

..5.. x .... = ...

Dice dots

For each row, complete the calculation to show
how many dots are on each dice.

$$30 \text{ dots} \div 6 \text{ dice} = 5 \text{ dots on each dice}$$

$$\underline{} \div \underline{} = \underline{5}$$

$$\underline{} \div \underline{} = \underline{5}$$

$$\underline{} \div \underline{} = \underline{5}$$

Dividing by 5

These 15 monkeys need to be split into 5 groups for gymnastics lessons. Complete the calculation to show how many monkeys will be in each group.

15 ÷ 5 =

Dividing by 5

Tan-tan wants to divide 20 bananas into 5 piles. Complete the calculation below to show many bananas will be in each pile.

$$20 \div 5 = \boxed{}$$

And how many in each pile if I divide 35 bananas into 5 piles?

$$35 \div 5 = \boxed{}$$

5 each

A family of 10 bears wants to ride the roller-coaster. Each car has seats for 5 animals. Complete the calculation to show how many cars the family needs so that every animal has a seat.

$$10 \div \boxed{} = 5$$

5 each

This car can carry 5 passengers. Complete the calculation to show how many cars are needed if there are 25 animals waiting.

$$25 \div \boxed{} = 5$$

ROLLER-COASTER RIDES THIS WAY!

And how many cars if there are **40** animals waiting?

$$40 \div \boxed{} = 5$$

Calculation match-up

Help Baz find the answers to these calculations. Draw a line to match each one with the correct answer.

$45 \div 5$

10

4

$20 \div 5$

$5 \div 5$

$30 \div 5$

5

9

2

$50 \div 5$

1

$10 \div 5$

$25 \div 5$

6

Right or wrong?

Check if Tig and Tan-tan have answered these calculations correctly. Put a ✔ or X in the boxes. Then, turn the page.

$10 \div 5 = 2$

$20 \div 5 = 5$

$25 \div 5 = 5$

$45 \div 5 = 9$

$0 \div 5 = 1$

$30 \div 5 = 7$

$35 \div 5 = 8$

$5 \div 5 = 0$

That's a tricky one!

$50 \div 5 = 10$

$15 \div 5 = 3$

Correcting calculations

Complete the other side of this page. Then, copy the calculations that are wrong into the blank boxes below, writing the correct answers instead.

Missing numbers

Write the missing numbers in the boxes
to complete these calculations.

$$10 \div \boxed{} = 5$$

$$30 \div \boxed{} = 5$$

$$45 \div \boxed{} = 5$$

$$5 \div \boxed{} = 5$$

$$35 \div \boxed{} = 5$$

$$20 \div \boxed{} = 5$$

Missing numbers

Write the missing numbers in the boxes
to complete these calculations.

$30 \div 5 = \boxed{}$

$\boxed{} \div 5 = 10$

$25 \div \boxed{} = 5$

$\boxed{} \div 5 = 4$

$40 \div \boxed{} = 8$

$45 \div 5 = \boxed{}$

Number wheel

Help Cheeky complete the number wheel. Divide each number by 5 to fill in the blank spaces.

35 20
25   5
30 ÷5 45
40   50
8 15 10

÷5

Forty divided by five is eight.

÷5

Sharing

Share out these 10 sandwiches equally onto 10 plates. Cross off each sandwich as you draw it on a plate, then complete the calculation below.

$$10 \div 10 = \boxed{}$$

each

Sharing

Help Baz share out these 20 bees equally into
10 hives. Cross off each bee as you draw it in
a hive, then complete the calculation below.

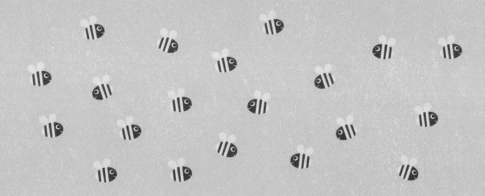

$$20 \div 10 = \boxed{}$$

each

Grouping

Help Tan-tan group these 30 bugs into 10s. Draw around the bugs in groups of 10, then count the groups to complete the calculation below.

That's a lot of bugs!

$$30 \div \boxed{} = 10$$

groups

Grouping

Help Ant group these 40 ants into 10s. Draw around the ants in groups of 10, then count the groups to complete the calculation below.

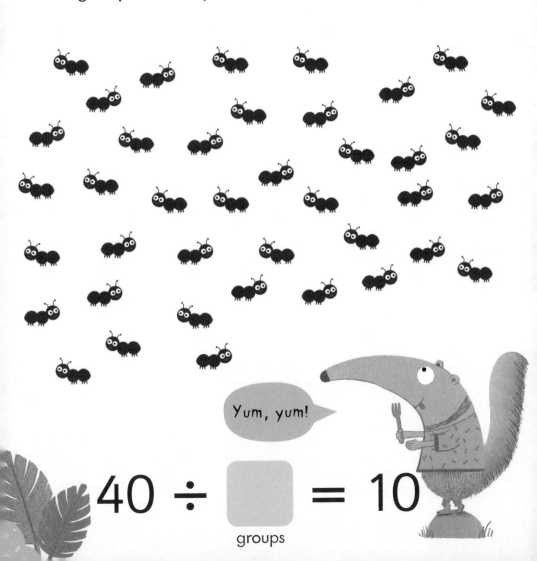

Yum, yum!

$$40 \div \boxed{} = 10$$

groups

Arrays

Fill in the blanks so that each array is described by both a multiplication and a division sentence.

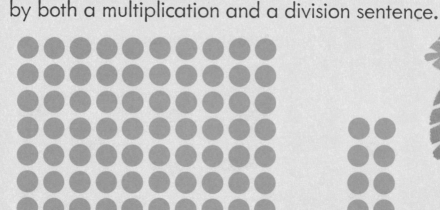

7 x ...... = 70

...... ÷ 10 = 7

...... x 10 = 20

20 ÷ ...... = 2

...... x 10 = 40

...... ÷ 10 = 4

Domino dots

For each row, complete the calculation to show
how many dots are on each domino.

$\underline{50}_{\text{dots}} \div \underline{5}_{\text{dominoes}} = \underline{10}_{\text{dots on each domino}}$

$\underline{} \div \underline{} = \underline{10}$

$\underline{} \div \underline{} = \underline{10}$

$\underline{} \div \underline{} = \underline{10}$

Dividing by 10

These 40 frogs need to be split into 10 groups for swimming lessons. Complete the calculation to show how many frogs will be in each group.

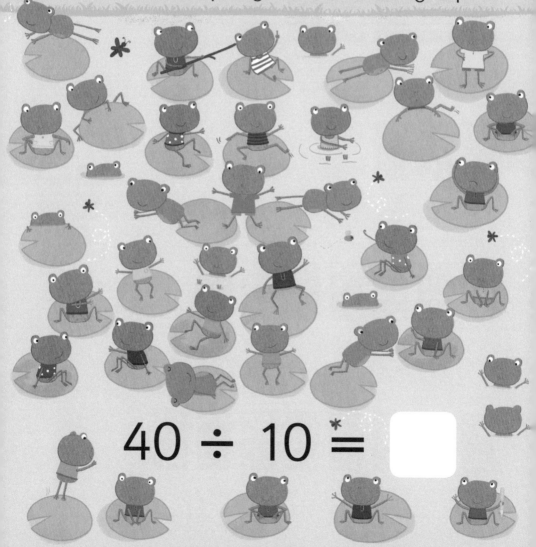

$$40 \div 10 = \boxed{}$$

Crock wants to divide 50 life jackets into 10 piles.
Complete the calculation below to show how
many life jackets will be in each pile.

$$50 \div 10 = \boxed{}$$

And how many in
each pile if I divide
100 life jackets
into 10 piles?

LIFE
JACKETS

$$100 \div 10 = \boxed{}$$

10 each

This party of 30 mice has arrived at Beaky's Buses. Each bus has seats for 10 animals. Complete the calculation to show many buses the party needs so that every animal has a seat.

$$30 \div \boxed{} = 10$$

10 each

This bus can carry 10 passengers. Complete the calculation to show how many trips are needed to carry 60 animals to the beach.

$$60 \div \boxed{} = 10$$

Beaky's Buses

And how many trips if 90 animals are going to the beach?

$$90 \div \boxed{} = 10$$

Calculation match-up

Help Baz find the answers to these calculations.
Draw a line to match each one with the
correct answer.

$50 \div 10$

3

2

8

$20 \div 10$

$80 \div 10$

$40 \div 10$

5

10

4

$70 \div 10$

$30 \div 10$

7

$100 \div 10$

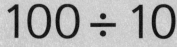

Right or wrong?

Check if Tan-tan and Tig have answered these calculations correctly. Put a ✔ or X in the boxes. Then, turn the page.

$60 \div 10 = 16$ ☐

$100 \div 10 = 10$ ☐

$30 \div 10 = 3$ ☐

$80 \div 10 = 18$ ☐

$90 \div 10 = 9$ ☐

$20 \div 10 = 3$ ☐

$10 \div 10 = 10$ ☐

$40 \div 10 = 4$ ☐

$50 \div 10 = 5$ ☐

$70 \div 10 = 70$ ☐

Let's get started!

Correcting calculations 52

Complete the other side of this page. Then, copy the calculations that are wrong into the blank boxes below, writing the correct answers instead.

Missing numbers

Write the missing numbers in the boxes
to complete these calculations.

$70 \div \boxed{} = 10$

$40 \div \boxed{} = 10$

$100 \div \boxed{} = 10$

$30 \div \boxed{} = 10$

$10 \div \boxed{} = 10$

$80 \div \boxed{} = 10$

Missing numbers

Write the missing numbers in the boxes
to complete these calculations.

$$80 \div 10 = \boxed{}$$

$$\boxed{} \div 10 = 6$$

$$50 \div \boxed{} = 5$$

$$\boxed{} \div 10 = 10$$

$$30 \div \boxed{} = 3$$

$$70 \div 10 = \boxed{}$$

Number wheel

Help Cheeky complete the number wheel. Divide each number by 10 to fill in the blank spaces.

90 20 80 50 ÷10 100 10 30 70 3 60 40

Thirty divided by ten is three.

÷10

Sharing

Help Lep and Crock share out these 9 drawings equally onto 3 boards. Cross off each drawing as you draw it on a board, then complete the calculation below.

$$9 \div 3 = \boxed{}$$

each

Sharing

Help Lem and Baz share out these 18 eggs equally into 3 frying pans. Cross off each egg as you draw it in a pan, then complete the calculation below.

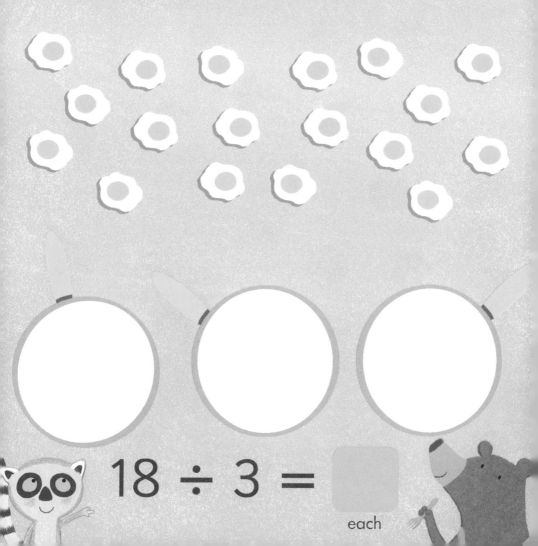

18 ÷ 3 =

each

Grouping

Help Tan-tan group these 27 mangoes into 3s.
Draw around the mangoes in groups of 3, then
count the groups to complete the calculation below.

They look tasty!

27 ÷ ☐ = 3

groups

Grouping

Help Ant group these 21 milk cartons into 3s. Draw around the cartons in groups of 3, then count the groups to complete the calculation below.

$$21 \div \boxed{} = 3$$

groups

Arrays

Fill in the blanks so that each array is described by both a multiplication and a division sentence.

$6 \times \ldots = 18$

$18 \div \ldots = 6$

$\ldots \times 3 = 12$

$12 \div \ldots = 4$

$\ldots \times 3 = 9$

$\ldots \div 3 = 3$

$9 \times \ldots = 27$

$\ldots \div 3 = 9$

Fact family

A fact family is a set of three numbers that can be divided or multiplied together. Fill in the blank spaces below to show the two dividing and two multiplying calculations for this fact family.

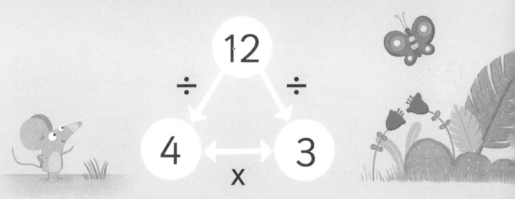

...12... ÷ .... = ...

...12... ÷ .... = ...

...4... x .... = ...

...3... x .... = ...

Fact family

Fill in the blank spaces below to show the
two dividing and two multiplying calculations
for this fact family.

18

÷ ÷

6 x **3**

.... ÷ ..6.. = ...

.... ÷ .... = ..6..

.... x .... = ..18..

..3.. x .... = ...

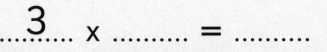

Fact family

A fact family is a set of three numbers that can be divided or multiplied together. Fill in the blank spaces below to show the two dividing and two multiplying calculations for this fact family.

24
÷ ÷
8 ⟷ 3
x

.... ÷ ..8.. = ...

.... ÷ .... = ..8..

.... x .... = ..24..

..3.. x .... = ...

Dice dots

For each row, complete the calculation to show
how many dots are on each dice.

15 dots $\div$ 5 dice $=$ 3 dots on each dice

_____ $\div$ _____ $=$ 3

_____ $\div$ _____ $=$ 3

_____ $\div$ _____ $=$ 3

These 21 mice need to be split into 3 groups for a party game. Complete the calculation to show how many mice will be in each group.

$$21 \div 3 = \boxed{}$$

Dividing by 3

This mouse wants to divide 15 birthday flowers into 3 vases. Complete the calculation below to show how many flowers will be in each vase.

$$15 \div 3 =$$

And how many in each vase if I divide 9 flowers into 3 vases?

$$9 \div 3 =$$

3 each

A party of 12 animals has arrived at Ant's Pirate Boat Trips. Each boat has space for 3 animals. Complete the calculation to show how many boats the party needs so that every animal has a place.

$$12 \div \boxed{} = 3$$

3 each

In Tig's Pirate Gift Shop, each treasure chest has space for 3 bags of chocolate coins. Complete the calculation to show how many chests are needed for 27 bags.

$$27 \div \boxed{} = 3$$

And how many chests are needed for 30 bags of chocolate coins?

GIFT SHOP

$$30 \div \boxed{} = 3$$

Calculation match-up

Help Baz find the answers to these calculations.
Draw a line to match each one with the
correct answer.

$12 \div 3$

1

2

3

$6 \div 3$

5

$24 \div 3$

$3 \div 3$

9

4

8

$9 \div 3$

$15 \div 3$

$27 \div 3$

Missing numbers

Write the missing numbers in the boxes
to complete these calculations.

$21 \div \boxed{} = 3$

$24 \div \boxed{} = 3$

$12 \div \boxed{} = 3$

$9 \div \boxed{} = 3$

$27 \div \boxed{} = 3$

$15 \div \boxed{} = 3$

Right or wrong?

Check if Tan-tan and Tig have answered these
calculations correctly. Put a ✔ or **X** in the boxes.
Then, turn the page.

$6 \div 3 = 3$ ☐ $21 \div 3 = 6$ ☐

$30 \div 3 = 11$ ☐ $12 \div 3 = 2$ ☐

$24 \div 3 = 8$ ☐ $9 \div 3 = 3$ ☐

$15 \div 3 = 5$ ☐ $18 \div 3 = 7$ ☐

$3 \div 3 = 1$ ☐

$27 \div 3 = 9$ ☐

Correcting calculations

Complete the other side of this page. Then, copy the calculations that are wrong into the blank boxes below, writing the correct answers instead.

Missing numbers

Write the missing numbers in the boxes
to complete these calculations.

$21 \div 3 = \boxed{}$

$\boxed{} \div 3 = 6$

$24 \div \boxed{} = 8$

$\boxed{} \div 3 = 4$

$15 \div \boxed{} = 5$

$27 \div 3 = \boxed{}$

Help Cheeky complete the number wheel. Divide each number by 3 to fill in the blank spaces.

Fifteen divided by three is five.

Sharing

Help Lep and Crock share out these 24 chocolates equally into 6 jars. Cross off each chocolate as you draw it in a jar, then complete the calculation below.

$$24 \div 6 = \boxed{}$$

each

Sharing

Help Lem and Baz share out these 12 watermelons equally into 6 boxes. Cross off each watermelon as you draw it in a box, then complete the calculation below.

$12 \div 6 =$

each

Grouping

Help Tan-tan group these 30 ice pops into 6s. Draw around the ice pops in groups of 6, then count the groups to complete the calculation below.

I hope they don't melt!

$$30 \div \boxed{} = 6$$

groups

Grouping

Help Ant group these 42 coins into 6s. Draw around the coins in groups of 6, then count the groups to complete the calculation below.

$$42 \div \boxed{} = 6$$

groups

Arrays

Fill in the blanks so that each array is described by both a multiplication and a division sentence.

...... x 6 = 42

42 ÷ ...... = 7

...... x 6 = 60

...... ÷ 6 = 10

4 x ...... = 24

...... ÷ 6 = 4

Fact family

A fact family is a set of three numbers that can be divided or multiplied together. Fill in the blank spaces below to show the two dividing and two multiplying calculations for this fact family.

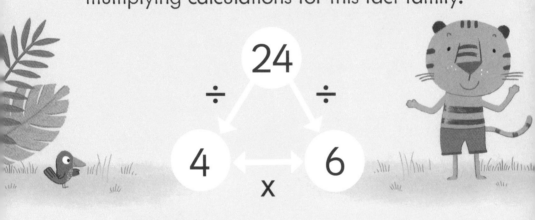

$$24 \div .... = ...$$

$$24 \div .... = ...$$

$$4 \times .... = ...$$

$$6 \times .... = ...$$

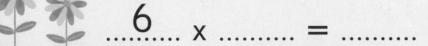

Fact family

Fill in the blank spaces below to show the
two dividing and two multiplying calculations
for this fact family.

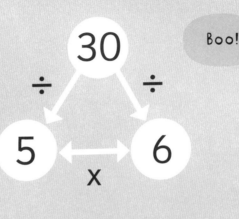

Boo!

$$\ldots \div \underline{5} = \ldots$$

$$\ldots \div \ldots = \underline{5}$$

$$\ldots \times \ldots = \underline{30}$$

$$\underline{6} \times \ldots = \ldots$$

Fact family

A fact family is a set of three numbers that can be divided or multiplied together. Fill in the blank spaces below to show the two dividing and two multiplying calculations for this fact family.

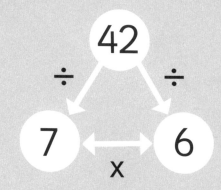

.... ÷ ...7... = ...

.... ÷ .... = ...7...

.... x .... = ..42...

...6... x .... = ...

Dice dots

For each row, complete the calculation to show
how many dots are on each dice.

$$12 \text{ dots} \div 2 \text{ dice} = 6 \text{ dots on each dice}$$

$$\underline{} \div \underline{} = \underline{6}$$

$$\underline{} \div \underline{} = \underline{6}$$

$$\underline{} \div \underline{} = \underline{6}$$

Dividing by 6

These 12 animals need to be divided into 6 groups for dancing lessons. Complete the calculation to find out how many animals will be in each group.

$$12 \div 6 = \boxed{}$$

Cheeky wants to divide 30 water bottles into 6 groups. Complete the calculation below to show how many bottles will be in each group.

$$30 \div 6 = \boxed{}$$

And how many in each group if **I** divide **48** bottles into 6 groups?

$$48 \div 6 = \boxed{}$$

This party of 18 animals has arrived at Lep's Café. Each table has seats for 6 animals. Complete the calculation to show how many tables are needed to seat all the animals.

$$18 \div \boxed{} = 6$$

Each cake stand has room for 6 cakes. Complete the calculation to show how many cake stands are needed for 42 cakes.

$$42 \div \boxed{} = 6$$

And how many cake stands are needed if there are **54** cakes?

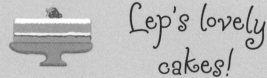

Lep's lovely cakes!

$$54 \div \boxed{} = 6$$

Calculation match-up

Help Baz find the answers to these calculations.
Draw a line to match each one with the
correct answer.

$12 \div 6$

10

2

$48 \div 6$

8

$54 \div 6$

6

$24 \div 6$

9

$60 \div 6$

7

$42 \div 6$

Hello, Tig!

4

$36 \div 6$

Right or wrong?

Check if Tig and Tan-tan have answered these
calculations correctly. Put a ✔ or ✗ in the boxes.
Then, turn the page.

$36 \div 6 = 6$ ☐ $24 \div 6 = 5$ ☐

$12 \div 6 = 2$ ☐ $0 \div 6 = 0$ ☐

$6 \div 6 = 1$ ☐ $42 \div 6 = 6$ ☐

$30 \div 6 = 4$ ☐ $60 \div 6 = 9$ ☐

$48 \div 6 = 7$ ☐

$18 \div 6 = 3$ ☐

Correcting calculations 90

Complete the other side of this page. Then, copy the calculations that are wrong into the blank boxes below, writing the correct answers instead.

Missing numbers

Write the missing numbers in the boxes
to complete these calculations.

$$24 \div \boxed{} = 6$$

$$42 \div \boxed{} = 6$$

$$18 \div \boxed{} = 6$$

$$6 \div \boxed{} = 6$$

$$12 \div \boxed{} = 6$$

$$60 \div \boxed{} = 6$$

Missing numbers

Write the missing numbers in the boxes
to complete these calculations.

$48 \div 6 = \boxed{}$

$\boxed{} \div 6 = 4$

$30 \div \boxed{} = 5$

$\boxed{} \div 6 = 10$

$18 \div \boxed{} = 3$

$12 \div 6 = \boxed{}$

Number wheel

Help Cheeky complete the number wheel. Divide each number by 6 to fill in the blank spaces.

12 30
54 6
36 ÷6 24
60 42
10 48 18

Sixty divided by six is ten.

÷6

Sharing

Help Lep and Crock share out these 8 candles equally onto 4 cakes. Cross off each candle as you draw it on a cake, then complete the calculation below.

8 ÷ 4 =

each

Sharing

Help Baz and Lem share out these 12 pencils equally into 4 pencil cases. Cross off each pencil as you draw it in a pencil case, then complete the calculation below.

$$12 \div 4 = \boxed{}$$

each

Grouping

Help Tan-tan group these 28 pears into 4s. Draw around the pears in groups of 4, then count the groups to complete the calculation below.

$$28 \div \boxed{} = 4$$

groups

Grouping

Help Ant group these 20 snakes into 4s. Draw around the snakes in groups of 4, then count the groups to complete the calculation below.

I hope they don't bite!

20 ÷ ☐ = 4

groups

Arrays

Fill in the blanks so that each array is described by both a multiplication and a division sentence.

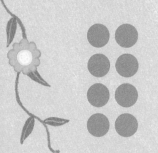

...... x 4 = 8

...... x 4 = 32

8 ÷ ...... = 2

...... ÷ 4 = 8

5 x ...... = 20

4 x ...... = 16

...... ÷ 4 = 5

16 ÷ ...... = 4

Fact family

A fact family is a set of three numbers that can be divided or multiplied together. Fill in the blank spaces below to show the two dividing and two multiplying calculations for this fact family.

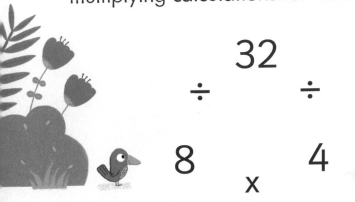

$$32$$

$$\div \qquad \div$$

$$8 \qquad 4$$

$$\times$$

..32.. ÷ .... = ...

..32.. ÷ .... = ...

..8.. × .... = ...

..4.. × .... = ...

Dice dots

For each row, complete the calculation to show
how many dots are on each dice.

$$32_{\text{dots}} \div 8_{\text{dice}} = 4_{\text{dots on each dice}}$$

That's a
tricky one!

$$\ldots \div \ldots = 4$$

$$\ldots \div \ldots = 4$$

$$\ldots \div \ldots = 4$$

Dividing by 4

These 28 parrots need to be divided into 4 groups for talking lessons. Complete the calculation to show how many parrots will be in each group.

$$28 \div 4 =$$

Dividing by 4

Baz wants to divide 16 text books into
4 piles. Complete the calculation to find out
how many text books will be in each pile.

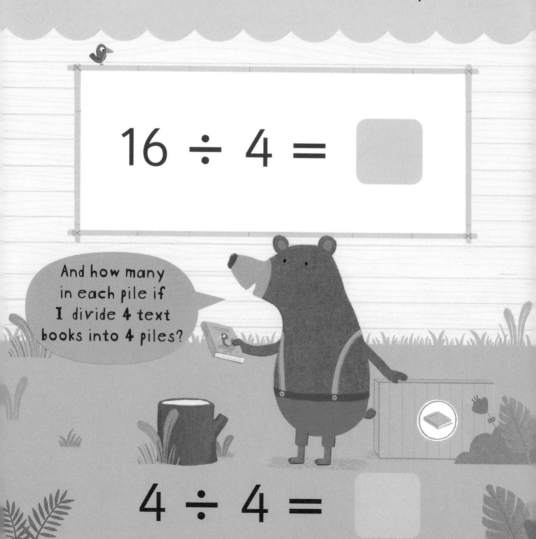

$$16 \div 4 = \boxed{}$$

And how many
in each pile if
I divide 4 text
books into 4 piles?

$$4 \div 4 = \boxed{}$$

4 each

A party of 24 animals has arrived at Lem's Raft Rental. Each raft has space for 4 animals. Complete the calculation to show how many rafts the party needs so that every animal has a place.

$$24 \div \boxed{} = 4$$

4 each

One box can hold 4 paddles. Complete the calculation to find out how many boxes are needed to hold 8 paddles.

$$8 \div \boxed{} = 4$$

And how many boxes are needed to hold 40 paddles?

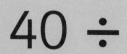

$$40 \div \boxed{} = 4$$

Calculation match-up

Help Baz find the answers to these calculations. Draw a line to match each one with the correct answer.

$16 \div 4$

1

2

4

$24 \div 4$

$36 \div 4$

$8 \div 4$

5

10

6

$4 \div 4$

$40 \div 4$

$20 \div 4$

9

Missing numbers

Write the missing numbers in the boxes
to complete these calculations.

$12 \div \boxed{} = 4$

$32 \div \boxed{} = 4$

$4 \div \boxed{} = 4$

$40 \div \boxed{} = 4$

$28 \div \boxed{} = 4$

$20 \div \boxed{} = 4$

Right or wrong?

Check if Tan-tan and Tig have answered these calculations correctly. Put a ✔ or X in the boxes. Then, turn the page.

$28 \div 4 = 6$ ☐

$4 \div 4 = 1$ ☐

$40 \div 4 = 10$ ☐

$24 \div 4 = 6$ ☐

$16 \div 4 = 4$ ☐

$32 \div 4 = 7$ ☐

$36 \div 4 = 8$ ☐

$12 \div 4 = 4$ ☐

$20 \div 4 = 4$ ☐

$8 \div 4 = 2$ ☐

Correcting calculations (108)

Complete the other side of this page. Then, copy
the calculations that are wrong into the blank boxes
below, writing the correct answers instead.

Missing numbers

Write the missing numbers in the
boxes to complete these calculations.

$8 \div 4 = \boxed{}$

$\boxed{} \div 4 = 4$

$4 \div \boxed{} = 1$

$\boxed{} \div 4 = 10$

$20 \div \boxed{} = 5$

$28 \div 4 = \boxed{}$

Number wheel

Help Cheeky complete the number wheel. Divide each number by 4 to fill in the blank spaces.

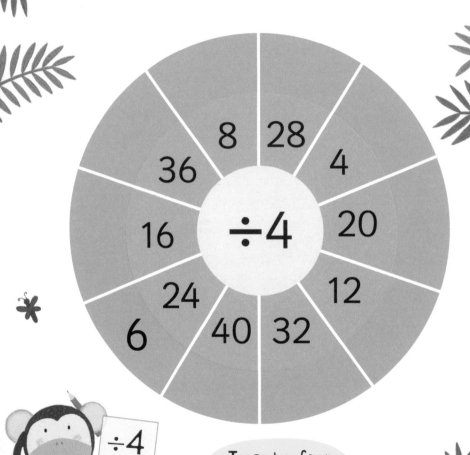

8 28

36 4

16 ÷4 20

24 12

6 40 32

÷4

Twenty-four divided by four is six.

Sharing

Help Crock share out these 8 lemons equally onto 8 plates. Cross off each lemon as you draw it on a plate, then complete the calculation below.

I know the answer!

$8 \div 8 =$

each

Sharing

Help Baz and Lem share out these 16 bottles equally into 8 boxes. Cross off each bottle as you draw it in a box, then complete the calculation below.

$16 \div 8 =$ ☐

each

Grouping

Help Tan-tan group these 48 flowers into 8s. Draw around the flowers in groups of 8, then count the groups to complete the calculation below.

$$48 \div \boxed{} = 8$$

groups

Grouping

Help Ant group these 64 flying bugs into 8s. Draw around the flying bugs in groups of 8, then count the groups to complete the calculation below.

64 ÷ [ ] = 8

groups

Arrays

Fill in the blanks so that each array is described
by both a multiplication and a division sentence.

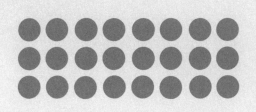

...... x 8 = 24

24 ÷ ...... = 3

...... x 8 = 56

...... ÷ 8 = 7

1 x ...... = 8

...... ÷ 8 = 1

Fact family

A fact family is a set of three numbers that can be divided or multiplied together. Fill in the blank spaces below to show the two dividing and two multiplying calculations for this fact family.

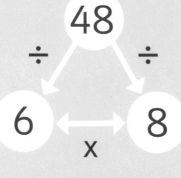

48 ÷ ÷

6 ⟷ 8

x

48 ÷ .... = ...

48 ÷ .... = ...

6 x .... = ...

8 x .... = ...

Fact family

Fill in the blank spaces below to show the
two dividing and two multiplying calculations
for this fact family.

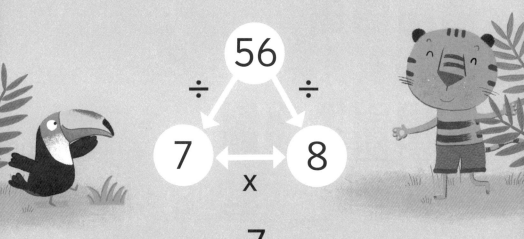

.... ÷ ...7... = ...

.... ÷ .... = ...7...

.... x .... = ...56...

...8... x .... = ...

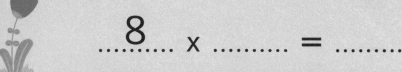

Domino dots

For each row, complete the calculation to show
how many dots are on each domino.

32 dots $\div$ 4 dominoes $=$ 8 dots on each domino

.... $\div$ .... $=$ 8

.... $\div$ .... $=$ 8

.... $\div$ .... $=$ 8

Dividing by 8

These 24 animals need to be split into 8 groups to rehearse for a play. Complete the calculation to show how many animals will be in each group.

$$24 \div 8 = \boxed{}$$

Dividing by 8

Cheeky needs to divide 64 props into 8 piles.
Complete the calculation below to show how
many props will be in each pile.

$64 \div 8 =$

And how many
in each pile if I
divide 80 props
into 8 piles?

PROPS

$80 \div 8 =$

8 each

Baz is trying to collect 32 fireflies and put them into jars. Each jar has room has 8 fireflies. Complete the calculation to show many jars he will need to catch all the fireflies.

$$32 \div \boxed{} = 8$$

8 each

The backpack on the table has space for 8 packed lunches. Complete the calculation to find out how many backpacks are needed for 56 packed lunches.

$$56 \div \boxed{} = 8$$

And how many backpacks are needed for 72 packed lunches?

$$72 \div \boxed{} = 8$$

Calculation match-up

Help Baz find the answers to these calculations. Draw a line to match each one with the correct answer.

$40 \div 8$

2

1

$24 \div 8$

7

$8 \div 8$

$16 \div 8$

$56 \div 8$

8

3

10

$64 \div 8$

$80 \div 8$

5

Missing numbers

Write the missing numbers in the boxes
to complete these calculations.

16 ÷ ☐ = 8

48 ÷ ☐ = 8

32 ÷ ☐ = 8

72 ÷ ☐ = 8

64 ÷ ☐ = 8

24 ÷ ☐ = 8

Right or wrong?

Check if Tan-tan and Tig have answered these
calculations correctly. Put a ✔ or X in the boxes.
Then, turn the page.

$48 \div 8 = 6$

$40 \div 8 = 7$

$32 \div 8 = 4$

$16 \div 8 = 2$

$56 \div 8 = 6$

$64 \div 8 = 8$

$8 \div 8 = 0$

$72 \div 8 = 10$

$80 \div 8 = 8$

$24 \div 8 = 3$

Correcting calculations

Complete the other side of this page. Then, copy the calculations that are wrong into the blank boxes below, writing the correct answers instead.

☐ ÷ ☐ = ☐

☐ ÷ ☐ = ☐

☐ ÷ ☐ = ☐

☐ ÷ ☐ = ☐

☐ ÷ ☐ = ☐

÷8

Missing numbers

Write the missing numbers in the boxes
to complete these calculations.

$$24 \div 8 = \boxed{}$$

$$\boxed{} \div 8 = 6$$

$$80 \div \boxed{} = 10$$

$$\boxed{} \div 8 = 8$$

$$16 \div \boxed{} = 2$$

$$72 \div 8 = \boxed{}$$

Number wheel

Help Cheeky complete the number wheel. Divide each number by 8 to fill in the blank spaces.

8 72 48 88 32 ÷8 16 80 56 10 24 40

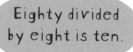

Eighty divided by eight is ten.

÷8

How many each?

Write the answers to these word questions in the boxes.

Cheeky has 12 bananas. She wants to divide them equally into 2 boxes. How many bananas would be in each box?

Lem has 25 marbles. She wants to divide them equally into 5 bags. How many marbles would be in each bag?

Tig has 70 badges. He wants to divide them equally into 10 boxes. How many badges would be in each box?

Baz has 24 flowers. He wants to divide them equally into 2 bunches. How many flowers would be in each bunch?

Froggy has 45 coins. She wants to divide them equally into 5 piles. How many coins would be in each pile?

How many groups?

Write the answers to these word questions in the boxes.

Lep has 14 lollipops. She wants to divide them into packs of 2. How many packs can she make?

Tan-tan has 10 tennis balls. She wants to divide them into tubes of 5. How many tubes can she fill?

Ant has 100 crayons. He wants to divide them into packs of 10. How many packs can he make?

Beaky has 18 cherries. He wants to divide them into bags of 2. How many bags can he make?

Crock has 55 wooden blocks. He wants to divide them into stacks of 5. How many stacks can he make?

Dividing by 3

Write the answers to these word questions in the boxes.

Lem has 30 candy canes, and wants to share them equally between 3 friends. How many candy canes will each friend get?

Crock is baking gingerbread men. He has 21 chocolate buttons and wants to stick 3 on each one. How many can he complete?

Froggy has 27 food pellets and needs to split them equally between 3 hamsters. How many pellets will each hamster get?

Ant has 12 toy soldiers and wants to divide them equally into 3 squads. How many toy soldiers will be in each squad?

Baz is planting sunflower seeds. He has 33 seeds and wants to plant 3 in each pot. How many pots can he fill?

Dividing by 6

Write the answers to these word questions in the boxes.

Cheeky has 54 playing cards. She must deal them equally between 6 players. How many cards will each player get?

Tan-tan is making pizza. She has 36 pieces of pepperoni and needs to put 6 on each pizza. How many pizzas can she make?

Tig has 12 carrots and wants to share them equally between 6 rabbits. How many carrots will each rabbit get?

Beaky has 18 counters and needs to share them equally between 6 players. How many counters will each player get?

Lep has 24 building blocks and wants to build towers that are 6 blocks high. How many towers can she make?

Dividing by 4

Write the answers to these word
questions in the boxes.

Tan-tan is making marmalade. She has 28
oranges and each jar of marmalade needs
4 oranges. How many jars can she make?

Lem has 8 packs of mints. She want to
divide the packs equally between 4 friends.
How many packs will each friend get?

Crock has 20 dice and needs to divide
them equally between 4 players. How
many dice will each player get?

Lep has 48 daffodil bulbs and wants
to plant them in rows of 4. How
many rows can she make?

Baz has exactly 16 minutes to complete
4 laps of the track. How many minutes
does he have to complete each lap?

Dividing by 8

Write the answers to these word questions in the boxes.

Tig has 56 daisies and wants to make them into 8 identical daisy-chains. How many daisies will be in each chain?

Froggy has 64 toy sheep and wants to divide them into herds of 8. How many herds can she make?

Ant is baking muffins. He has 80 raisins and wants to put 8 into each muffin. How many muffins can he make?

Beaky has 16 minutes to swim 8 lengths of the pool. How many minutes does he have to swim each length?

Cheeky has 40 peanuts and wants to share them equally between 8 parrots. How many peanuts will each parrot get?

Space for calculations

Space for calculations

Space for calculations

Answers

Sharing 1

Help Crock and Lep share out these 6 cupcakes equally onto 2 plates. Cross off each cupcake as you draw it on a plate, then complete the calculation below.

$6 \div 2 = 3$ each

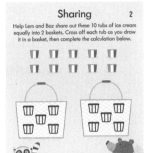

Sharing 2

Help Lem and Baz share out these 10 tubs of ice cream equally into 2 baskets. Cross off each tub as you draw it in a basket, then complete the calculation below.

$10 \div 2 = 5$ each

Grouping 3

How many pairs of socks does Baz have? Draw around these 12 socks in groups of 2, then count the groups to complete the calculation below.

$12 \div 6 = 2$ pairs

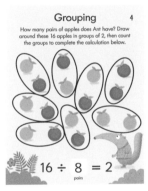

Grouping 4

How many pairs of apples does Ant have? Draw around these 16 apples in groups of 2, then count the groups to complete the calculation below.

$16 \div 8 = 2$ pairs

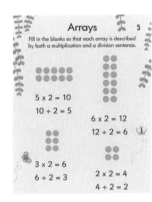

Arrays 5

Fill in the blanks so that each array is described by both a multiplication and a division sentence.

$5 \times 2 = 10$
$10 \div 2 = 5$

$6 \times 2 = 12$
$12 \div 2 = 6$

$3 \times 2 = 6$
$6 \div 2 = 3$

$2 \times 2 = 4$
$4 \div 2 = 2$

Fact family 6

A fact family is a set of three numbers that can be divided or multiplied together. Fill in the blank spaces below to show the two dividing and two multiplying calculations for this fact family.

$6 \div 3 \quad \div 2$

$6 \div 3 = 2$
$6 \div 2 = 3$
$3 \times 2 = 6$
$2 \times 3 = 6$

Fact family 7

Fill in the blank spaces below to show the two dividing and two multiplying calculations for this fact family.

$8 \div 4 \quad \div 2$

$8 \div 4 = 2$
$8 \div 2 = 4$
$4 \times 2 = 8$
$2 \times 4 = 8$

Fact family 8

A fact family is a set of three numbers that can be divided or multiplied together. Fill in the blank spaces below to show the two dividing and two multiplying calculations for this fact family.

$10 \div 5 \quad \div 2$

$10 \div 5 = 2$
$10 \div 2 = 5$
$5 \times 2 = 10$
$2 \times 5 = 10$

Fact family 9

Fill in the blank spaces below to show the two dividing and two multiplying calculations for this fact family.

$12 \div 6 \quad \div 2$

$12 \div 6 = 2$
$12 \div 2 = 6$
$6 \times 2 = 12$
$2 \times 6 = 12$

Answers

Dice dots 10

For each row, complete the calculation to show how many dots are on each dice.

6 dots $÷ 3$ dice $= 2$ dots on each dice

$12 ÷ 6 = 2$

$20 ÷ 10 = 2$

$16 ÷ 8 = 2$

Dividing by 2 11

These 18 tiger cubs need to be divided into 2 teams for a game in the park. Complete the calculation to show how many cubs will be in each team.

$18 ÷ 2 = 9$

Dividing by 2 12

Lem wants to divide 8 sports jerseys into 2 piles. Complete the calculation below to show how many jerseys will be in each pile.

$8 ÷ 2 = 4$

And how many in each pile if I divide 14 jerseys into 2 piles?

$14 ÷ 2 = 7$

2 each 13

A party of 16 animals has arrived at Crock's Canoe Club. Each canoe has seats for 2 animals. Complete the calculation to show how many canoes the party needs so that every animal has a seat.

$16 ÷ 8 = 2$

2 each 14

This canoe can carry 2 passengers. Complete the calculation to find out how many trips are needed to carry 20 animals across the river.

$20 ÷ 10 = 2$

And how many trips if 12 animals want to cross back again?

$12 ÷ 6 = 2$

Calculation match-up 15

Help Baz find the answers to these calculations. Draw a line to match each one with the correct answer.

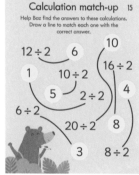

$12 ÷ 2$ 6   10
$16 ÷ 2$
1   $10 ÷ 2$
5   $2 ÷ 2$ 4
$6 ÷ 2$
$20 ÷ 2$ 8
3   $8 ÷ 2$

Missing numbers 16

Write the missing numbers in the boxes to complete these calculations.

$4 ÷ 2 = 2$

$20 ÷ 10 = 2$

$8 ÷ 4 = 2$

$12 ÷ 6 = 2$

$2 ÷ 1 = 2$

$16 ÷ 8 = 2$

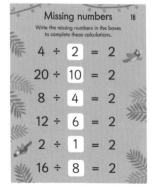

Right or wrong? 17

Check if Tig and Tan-tan answered these calculations correctly. Put a ✓ or X in the boxes. Then, turn the page.

$10 ÷ 2 = 4$ X $12 ÷ 2 = 6$ ✓

$4 ÷ 2 = 2$ ✓ $18 ÷ 2 = 8$ X

$14 ÷ 2 = 5$ X $6 ÷ 2 = 3$ ✓

$16 ÷ 2 = 8$ ✓ $20 ÷ 2 = 11$ X

$8 ÷ 2 = 4$ ✓

$0 ÷ 2 = 1$ X

Correcting calculations 18

Complete the other side of this page. Then, copy the calculations that are wrong into the blank boxes below, writing the correct answers instead.

$10 ÷ 2 = 5$

$14 ÷ 2 = 7$

$0 ÷ 2 = 0$

$18 ÷ 2 = 9$

$20 ÷ 2 = 10$

Answers

Missing numbers 19

Write the missing numbers in the boxes to complete these calculations.

$18 \div 2 = 9$

$10 \div 2 = 5$

$8 \div 2 = 4$

$20 \div 2 = 10$

$16 \div 2 = 8$

$4 \div 2 = 2$

Number wheel 20

Help Cheeky complete the number wheel. Divide each number by 2 to fill in the blank spaces.

7 10
9 14 20 8
18 16
2 4 ÷2 6 3
12 10
6 8 2 5
4 1

Twelve divides by two is six.

÷2

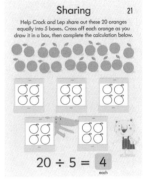

Sharing 21

Help Crock and Lep share out these 20 oranges equally into 5 boxes. Cross off each orange as you draw it in a box, then complete the calculation below.

$20 \div 5 = 4$

each

Sharing 22

Help Baz and Lem share out these 25 berries equally into 5 bowls. Cross off each berry as you draw it in a bowl, then complete the calculation below.

$25 \div 5 = 5$

each

Grouping 23

Help Tan-tan group these 30 bananas into 5s. Draw around the bananas in groups of 5, then count the groups to complete the calculation below.

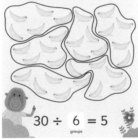

$30 \div 6 = 5$

groups

Grouping 24

Help Ant group these 15 pineapples into 5s. Draw around the pineapples in groups of 5, then count the groups to complete the calculation below.

$15 \div 3 = 5$

groups

Arrays 25

Fill in the blanks so that each array is described by both a multiplication and a division sentence.

$1 \times 5 = 5$

$5 \div 5 = 1$

$6 \times 5 = 30$

$30 \div 5 = 6$

$3 \times 5 = 15$

$15 \div 5 = 3$

$9 \times 5 = 45$

$45 \div 5 = 9$

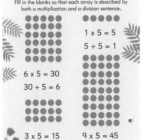

Fact family 26

A fact family is a set of three numbers that can be divided or multiplied together. Fill in the blank spaces below to show the two dividing and two multiplying calculations for this fact family.

15
÷   ÷
3 ←——→ 5
×

$15 \div 3 = 5$

$15 \div 5 = 3$

$3 \times 5 = 15$

$5 \times 3 = 15$

Fact family 27

Fill in the blank spaces below to show the two dividing and two multiplying calculations for this fact family.

20
÷   ÷
4   5
×

$20 \div 4 = 5$

$20 \div 5 = 4$

$4 \times 5 = 20$

$5 \times 4 = 20$

Answers

Fact family   28

A fact family is a set of three numbers that can be divided or multiplied together. Fill in the blank spaces below to show the two dividing and two multiplying calculations for this fact family.

50
÷ △ ÷
10   x   5

$50 ÷ 10 = 5$

$50 ÷ 5 = 10$

$10 × 5 = 50$

$5 × 10 = 50$

Dice dots   29

For each row, complete the calculation to show how many dots are on each dice.

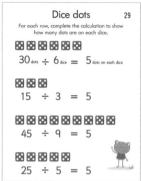

30 dots $÷ 6$ dice $= 5$ dots on each dice

$15 ÷ 3 = 5$

$45 ÷ 9 = 5$

$25 ÷ 5 = 5$

Dividing by 5   30

These 15 monkeys need to be split into 5 groups for gymnastics lessons. Complete the calculation to show how many monkeys will be in each group.

$15 ÷ 5 = \boxed{3}$

Dividing by 5   31

Tan-tan wants to divide 20 bananas into 5 piles. Complete the calculation below to show many bananas will be in each pile.

$20 ÷ 5 = \boxed{4}$

And how many in each pile if I divide 35 bananas into 5 piles?

$35 ÷ 5 = \boxed{7}$

5 each   32

A family of 10 bears wants to ride the roller-coaster. Each car has seats for 5 animals. Complete the calculation to show how many cars the family needs so that every animal has a seat.

Entrance

$10 ÷ \boxed{2} = 5$

5 each   33

This car can carry 5 passengers. Complete the calculation to show how many cars are needed if there are 25 animals waiting.

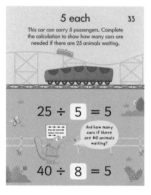

$25 ÷ \boxed{5} = 5$

And how many cars if there are 40 animals waiting?

$40 ÷ \boxed{8} = 5$

Calculation match-up   34

Help Baz find the answers to these calculations. Draw a line to match each one with the correct answer.

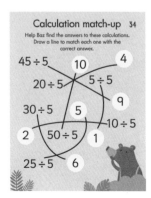

$45 ÷ 5$ — 10
4
$20 ÷ 5$ — $5 ÷ 5$
$30 ÷ 5$ — 9
5
2 — $50 ÷ 5$ — $10 ÷ 5$
1
$25 ÷ 5$ — 6

Right or wrong?   35

Check if Tig and Tan-tan have answered these calculations correctly. Put a ✓ or ✗ in the boxes. Then, turn the page.

$10 ÷ 5 = 2$ ✓ $20 ÷ 5 = 5$ ✗

$25 ÷ 5 = 5$ ✓ $45 ÷ 5 = 9$ ✓

$0 ÷ 5 = 1$ ✗ $30 ÷ 5 = 7$ ✗

$35 ÷ 5 = 8$ ✗ $5 ÷ 5 = 0$ ✗

$50 ÷ 5 = 10$ ✓

$15 ÷ 5 = 3$ ✓

Correcting calculations   36

Complete the other side of this page. Then, copy the calculations that are wrong into the blank boxes below, writing the correct answers instead.

$0 ÷ 5 = \boxed{0}$

$35 ÷ 5 = \boxed{7}$

$20 ÷ 5 = \boxed{4}$

$30 ÷ 5 = \boxed{6}$

$5 ÷ 5 = \boxed{1}$

Answers

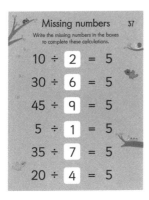

Missing numbers 37

Write the missing numbers in the boxes to complete these calculations.

$10 \div \boxed{2} = 5$

$30 \div \boxed{6} = 5$

$45 \div \boxed{9} = 5$

$5 \div \boxed{1} = 5$

$35 \div \boxed{7} = 5$

$20 \div \boxed{4} = 5$

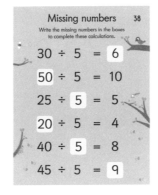

Missing numbers 38

Write the missing numbers in the boxes to complete these calculations.

$30 \div 5 = \boxed{6}$

$50 \div 5 = 10$

$25 \div \boxed{5} = 5$

$20 \div \boxed{5} = 4$

$40 \div \boxed{5} = 8$

$45 \div 5 = \boxed{9}$

Number wheel 39

Help Cheeky complete the number wheel. Divide each number by 5 to fill in the blank spaces.

Forty divided by five is eight.

$\div 5$

Sharing 40

Share out these 10 sandwiches equally onto 10 plates. Cross off each sandwich as you draw it on a plate, then complete the calculation below.

$10 \div 10 = \boxed{1}$ each

Sharing 41

Help Baz share out these 20 bees equally into 10 hives. Cross off each bee as you draw it in a hive, then complete the calculation below.

$20 \div 10 = \boxed{2}$ each

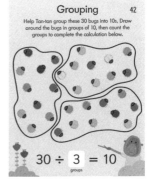

Grouping 42

Help Tan-tan group these 30 bugs into 10s. Draw around the bugs in groups of 10, then count the groups to complete the calculation below.

$30 \div \boxed{3} = 10$ groups

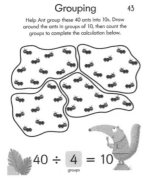

Grouping 43

Help Ant group these 40 ants into 10s. Draw around the ants in groups of 10, then count the groups to complete the calculation below.

$40 \div \boxed{4} = 10$ groups

Arrays 44

Fill in the blanks so that each array is described by both a multiplication and a division sentence.

$7 \times 10 = 70$

$70 \div 10 = 7$

$4 \times 10 = 40$

$40 \div 10 = 4$

$2 \times 10 = 20$

$20 \div 10 = 2$

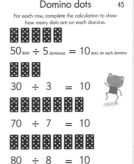

Domino dots 45

For each row, complete the calculation to show how many dots are on each domino.

$50_{\text{dots}} \div 5_{\text{dominoes}} = 10_{\text{dots on each domino}}$

$30 \div 3 = 10$

$70 \div 7 = 10$

$80 \div 8 = 10$

Answers

Dividing by 10 46

These 40 frogs need to be split into 10 groups for swimming lessons. Complete the calculation to show how many frogs will be in each group.

$40 \div 10 = 4$

Dividing by 10 47

Crock wants to divide 50 life jackets into 10 piles. Complete the calculation below to show how many life jackets will be in each pile.

$50 \div 10 = 5$

And how many in each pile if I divide 100 life jackets into 10 piles?

$100 \div 10 = 10$

10 each 48

This party of 30 mice has arrived at Beaky's Buses. Each bus has seats for 10 animals. Complete the calculation to show many buses the party needs so that every animal has a seat.

$30 \div 3 = 10$

10 each 49

This bus can carry 10 passengers. Complete the calculation to show how many trips are needed to carry 60 animals to the beach.

$60 \div 6 = 10$

And how many trips if 90 animals are going to the beach?

$90 \div 9 = 10$

Calculation match-up 50

Help Baz find the answers to these calculations. Draw a line to match each one with the correct answer.

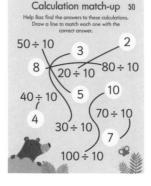

$50 \div 10$ 3   2
8   $20 \div 10$ $80 \div 10$
$40 \div 10$ 5   10
4   $70 \div 10$
$30 \div 10$ 7
$100 \div 10$

Right or wrong? 51

Check if Tan-tan and Tig have answered these calculations correctly. Put a ✓ or X in the boxes. Then, turn the page.

$60 \div 10 = 16$ **X** $100 \div 10 = 10$ **✓**

$30 \div 10 = 3$ **✓** $80 \div 10 = 18$ **X**

$90 \div 10 = 9$ **✓** $20 \div 10 = 3$ **X**

$10 \div 10 = 10$ **X** $40 \div 10 = 4$ **✓**

$50 \div 10 = 5$ **✓**

$70 \div 10 = 70$ **X**

Correcting calculations 52

Complete the other side of this page. Then, copy the calculations that are wrong into the blank boxes below, writing the correct answers instead.

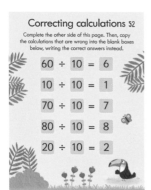

$60 \div 10 = 6$

$10 \div 10 = 1$

$70 \div 10 = 7$

$80 \div 10 = 8$

$20 \div 10 = 2$

Missing numbers 53

Write the missing numbers in the boxes to complete these calculations.

$70 \div 7 = 10$

$40 \div 4 = 10$

$100 \div 10 = 10$

$30 \div 3 = 10$

$10 \div 1 = 10$

$80 \div 8 = 10$

Missing numbers 54

Write the missing numbers in the boxes to complete these calculations.

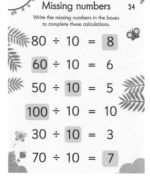

$80 \div 10 = 8$

$60 \div 10 = 6$

$50 \div 10 = 5$

$100 \div 10 = 10$

$30 \div 10 = 3$

$70 \div 10 = 7$

Answers

Number wheel 55

Help Cheeky complete the number wheel. Divide each number by 10 to fill in the blank spaces.

9 2
5 90 20 8
50 80
1 10 ÷10 100 10
30 70
3 60 40 7
6 4

Thirty divided by ten is three.

÷10

Sharing 56

Help Lep and Crock share out these 9 drawings equally onto 3 boards. Cross off each drawing as you draw it on a board, then complete the calculation below.

$9 \div 3 = 3$ each

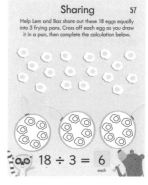

Sharing 57

Help Lem and Baz share out these 18 eggs equally into 3 frying pans. Cross off each egg as you draw it in a pan, then complete the calculation below.

$18 \div 3 = 6$ each

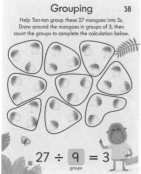

Grouping 58

Help Tan-tan group these 27 mangoes into 3s. Draw around the mangoes in groups of 3, then count the groups to complete the calculation below.

$27 \div 9 = 3$ groups

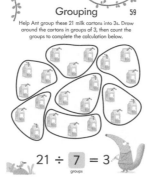

Grouping 59

Help Ant group these 21 milk cartons into 3s. Draw around the cartons in groups of 3, then count the groups to complete the calculation below.

$21 \div 7 = 3$ groups

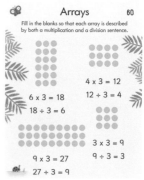

Arrays 60

Fill in the blanks so that each array is described by both a multiplication and a division sentence.

$4 \times 3 = 12$
$12 \div 3 = 4$
$6 \times 3 = 18$
$18 \div 3 = 6$

$3 \times 3 = 9$
$9 \div 3 = 3$
$9 \times 3 = 27$
$27 \div 3 = 9$

Fact family 61

A fact family is a set of three numbers that can be divided or multiplied together. Fill in the blank spaces below to show the two dividing and two multiplying calculations for this fact family.

12
÷ ÷
4 x 3

$12 \div 4 = 3$
$12 \div 3 = 4$
$4 \times 3 = 12$
$3 \times 4 = 12$

Fact family 62

Fill in the blank spaces below to show the two dividing and two multiplying calculations for this fact family.

18
÷ ÷
6 x 3

$18 \div 6 = 3$
$18 \div 3 = 6$
$6 \times 3 = 18$
$3 \times 6 = 18$

Fact family 63

A fact family is a set of three numbers that can be divided or multiplied together. Fill in the blank spaces below to show the two dividing and two multiplying calculations for this fact family.

24
÷ ÷
8 x 3

$24 \div 8 = 3$
$24 \div 3 = 8$
$8 \times 3 = 24$
$3 \times 8 = 24$

Answers

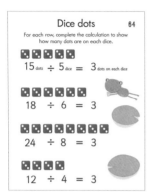

Dice dots 64

For each row, complete the calculation to show how many dots are on each dice.

$15 \text{ dots} \div 5 \text{ dice} = 3 \text{ dots on each dice}$

$18 \div 6 = 3$

$24 \div 8 = 3$

$12 \div 4 = 3$

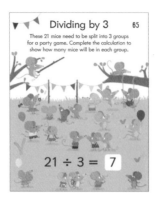

Dividing by 3 65

These 21 mice need to be split into 3 groups for a party game. Complete the calculation to show how many mice will be in each group.

$21 \div 3 = \boxed{7}$

Dividing by 3 66

This mouse wants to divide 15 birthday flowers into 3 vases. Complete the calculation below to show how many flowers will be in each vase.

$15 \div 3 = 5$

And how many in each vase if I divide 9 flowers into 3 vases?

$9 \div 3 = 3$

3 each 67

A party of 12 animals has arrived at Ant's Pirate Boat Trips. Each boat has space for 3 animals. Complete the calculation to show how many boats the party needs so that every animal has a place.

$12 \div \boxed{4} = 3$

3 each 68

In Tig's Pirate Gift Shop, each treasure chest has space for 3 bags of chocolate coins. Complete the calculation to show how many chests are needed for 27 bags.

$27 \div \boxed{9} = 3$

And how many chests are needed for 30 bags of chocolate coins?

GIFT SHOP

$30 \div \boxed{10} = 3$

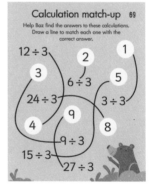

Calculation match-up 69

Help Baz find the answers to these calculations. Draw a line to match each one with the correct answer.

$12 \div 3$ 2   1
3   $6 \div 3$ 5
$24 \div 3$ 9 $3 \div 3$
4   8
$9 \div 3$
$15 \div 3$ $27 \div 3$

Missing numbers 70

Write the missing numbers in the boxes to complete these calculations.

$21 \div \boxed{7} = 3$

$24 \div \boxed{8} = 3$

$12 \div \boxed{4} = 3$

$9 \div \boxed{3} = 3$

$27 \div \boxed{9} = 3$

$15 \div \boxed{5} = 3$

Right or wrong? 71

Check if Tan-tan and Tig have answered these calculations correctly. Put a ✔ or ✗ in the boxes. Then, turn the page.

$6 \div 3 = 3$ ✗ $21 \div 3 = 6$ ✗

$30 \div 3 = 11$ ✗ $12 \div 3 = 2$ ✗

$24 \div 3 = 8$ ✔ $9 \div 3 = 3$ ✔

$15 \div 3 = 5$ ✔ $18 \div 3 = 7$ ✗

$3 \div 3 = 1$ ✔

$27 \div 3 = 9$ ✔

Correcting calculations 72

Complete the other side of this page. Then, copy the calculations that are wrong into the blank boxes below, writing the correct answers instead.

$6 \div 3 = 2$

$30 \div 3 = 10$

$21 \div 3 = 7$

$12 \div 3 = 4$

$18 \div 3 = 6$

Answers

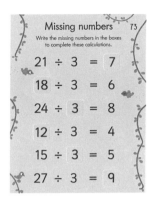

Missing numbers 73

Write the missing numbers in the boxes to complete these calculations.

$21 \div 3 = 7$

$18 \div 3 = 6$

$24 \div 3 = 8$

$12 \div 3 = 4$

$15 \div 3 = 5$

$27 \div 3 = 9$

Number wheel 74

Help Cheeky complete the number wheel. Divide each number by 3 to fill in the blank spaces.

10 6
2 30 18 1
6 ÷3 3
8 24 27 9
15 9
5 12 21 3
4 7

Fifteen divided by three is five.

÷3

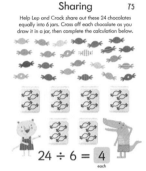

Sharing 75

Help Lep and Crock share out these 24 chocolates equally into 6 jars. Cross off each chocolate as you draw it in a jar, then complete the calculation below.

$24 \div 6 = 4$
each

Sharing 76

Help Lem and Baz share out these 12 watermelons equally into 6 boxes. Cross off each watermelon as you draw it in a box, then complete the calculation below.

$12 \div 6 = 2$
each

Grouping 77

Help Tan-tan group these 30 ice pops into 6s. Draw around the ice pops in groups of 6, then count the groups to complete the calculation below.

$30 \div 5 = 6$
groups

Grouping 78

Help Ant group these 42 coins into 6s. Draw around the coins in groups of 6, then count the groups to complete the calculation below.

$42 \div 7 = 6$
groups

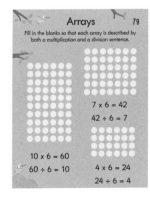

Arrays 79

Fill in the blanks so that each array is described by both a multiplication and a division sentence.

$7 \times 6 = 42$

$42 \div 6 = 7$

$10 \times 6 = 60$

$60 \div 6 = 10$

$4 \times 6 = 24$

$24 \div 6 = 4$

Fact family 80

A fact family is a set of three numbers that can be divided or multiplied together. Fill in the blank spaces below to show the two dividing and two multiplying calculations for this fact family.

24
÷   ÷
4   x   6

$24 \div 4 = 6$

$24 \div 6 = 4$

$4 \times 6 = 24$

$6 \times 4 = 24$

Fact family 81

Fill in the blank spaces below to show the two dividing and two multiplying calculations for this fact family.

30
÷   ÷
5   x   6

$30 \div 5 = 6$

$30 \div 6 = 5$

$5 \times 6 = 30$

$6 \times 5 = 30$

Answers

Fact family 82

A fact family is a set of three numbers that can be divided or multiplied together. Fill in the blank spaces below to show the two dividing and two multiplying calculations for this fact family.

42 ÷

7   x   6

42 ÷ 7 = 6

42 ÷ 6 = 7

7 x 6 = 42

6 x 7 = 42

Dice dots 83

For each row, complete the calculation to show how many dots are on each dice.

12 dots ÷ 2 dice = 6 dots on each dice

36 ÷ 6 = 6

24 ÷ 4 = 6

60 ÷ 10 = 6

Dividing by 6 84

These 12 animals need to be divided into 6 groups for dancing lessons. Complete the calculation to find out how many animals will be in each group.

12 ÷ 6 = 2

Dividing by 6 85

Cheeky wants to divide 30 water bottles into 6 groups. Complete the calculation below to show how many bottles will be in each group.

30 ÷ 6 = 5

And how many in each group if I divide 48 bottles into 6 groups?

48 ÷ 6 = 8

6 each 86

This party of 18 animals has arrived at Lep's Café. Each table has seats for 6 animals. Complete the calculation to show how many tables are needed to seat all the animals.

18 ÷ 3 = 6

6 each 87

Each cake stand has room for 6 cakes. Complete the calculation to show how many cake stands are needed for 42 cakes.

42 ÷ 7 = 6

And how many cake stands are needed if there are 54 cakes?

Lep's lovely cakes!

54 ÷ 9 = 6

Calculation match-up 88

Help Baz find the answers to these calculations. Draw a line to match each one with the correct answer.

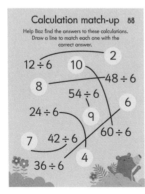

12 ÷ 6   2
              10
8   48 ÷ 6
        54 ÷ 6
24 ÷ 6   6
            9
        60 ÷ 6
7   42 ÷ 6
              4
36 ÷ 6

Right or wrong? 89

Check if Tig and Tan-tan have answered these calculations correctly. Put a ✓ or ✗ in the boxes. Then, turn the page.

36 ÷ 6 = 6 ✓   24 ÷ 6 = 5 ✗

12 ÷ 6 = 2 ✓   0 ÷ 6 = 0 ✓

6 ÷ 6 = 1 ✓   42 ÷ 6 = 6 ✗

30 ÷ 6 = 4 ✗   60 ÷ 6 = 9 ✗

48 ÷ 6 = 7 ✗

18 ÷ 6 = 3 ✓

Correcting calculations 90

Complete the other side of this page. Then, copy the calculations that are wrong into the blank boxes below, writing the correct answers instead.

30 ÷ 6 = 5

48 ÷ 6 = 8

24 ÷ 6 = 4

42 ÷ 6 = 7

60 ÷ 6 = 10

Answers

Missing numbers 91

Write the missing numbers in the boxes to complete these calculations.

$24 \div 4 = 6$

$42 \div 7 = 6$

$18 \div 3 = 6$

$6 \div 1 = 6$

$12 \div 2 = 6$

$60 \div 10 = 6$

Missing numbers 92

Write the missing numbers in the boxes to complete these calculations.

$48 \div 6 = 8$

$24 \div 6 = 4$

$30 \div 6 = 5$

$60 \div 6 = 10$

$18 \div 6 = 3$

$12 \div 6 = 2$

Number wheel 93

Help Cheeky complete the number wheel. Divide each number by 6 to fill in the blank spaces.

Sixty divided by six is ten.

$\div 6$

Sharing 94

Help Lep and Crock share out these 8 candles equally onto 4 cakes. Cross off each candle as you draw it on a cake, then complete the calculation below.

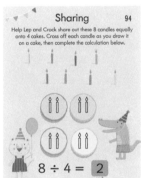

$8 \div 4 = 2$
each

Sharing 95

Help Baz and Lem share out these 12 pencils equally into 4 pencil cases. Cross off each pencil as you draw it in a pencil case, then complete the calculation below.

$12 \div 4 = 3$
each

Grouping 96

Help Tan-tan group these 28 pears into 4s. Draw around the pears in groups of 4, then count the groups to complete the calculation below.

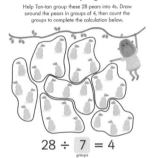

$28 \div 7 = 4$
groups

Grouping 97

Help Ant group these 20 snakes into 4s. Draw around the snakes in groups of 4, then count the groups to complete the calculation below.

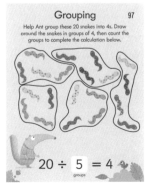

$20 \div 5 = 4$
groups

Arrays 98

Fill in the blanks so that each array is described by both a multiplication and a division sentence.

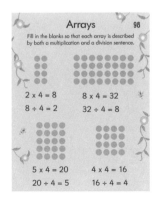

$2 \times 4 = 8$ $\qquad$ $8 \times 4 = 32$

$8 \div 4 = 2$ $\qquad$ $32 \div 4 = 8$

$5 \times 4 = 20$ $\qquad$ $4 \times 4 = 16$

$20 \div 4 = 5$ $\qquad$ $16 \div 4 = 4$

Fact family 99

A fact family is a set of three numbers that can be divided or multiplied together. Fill in the blank spaces below to show the two dividing and two multiplying calculations for this fact family.

32

$\div$ $\qquad$ $\div$

8 $\qquad$ 4

x

$32 \div 8 = 4$

$32 \div 4 = 8$

$8 \times 4 = 32$

$4 \times 8 = 32$

Answers

Dice dots　100

For each row, complete the calculation to show
many dots are on each dice.

$32_{dots} \div 8_{dice} = 4_{dots\ on\ each\ dice}$

$16 \div 4 = 4$

$36 \div 9 = 4$

$28 \div 7 = 4$

Dividing by 4　101

These 28 parrots need to be divided into 4 groups
for talking lessons. Complete the calculation to
show how many parrots will be in each group.

$28 \div 4 = 7$

Dividing by 4　102

Baz wants to divide 16 text books into
4 piles. Complete the calculation to find out
how many text books will be in each pile.

$16 \div 4 = 4$

And how many
in each pile if
I divide 4 text
books into 4 piles?

$4 \div 4 = 1$

4 each　103

A party of 24 animals has arrived at Lem's Raft
Rental. Each raft has space for 4 animals. Complete
the calculation to show how many rafts the party
needs so that every animal has a place.

LEM'S
RAFT
RENTAL

$24 \div 6 = 4$

4 each　104

One box can hold 4 paddles. Complete the
calculation to find out how many boxes are
needed to hold 8 paddles.

$8 \div 2 = 4$

And how many
boxes are
needed to hold
40 paddles?

$40 \div 10 = 4$

Calculation match-up　105

Help Baz find the answers to these calculations.
Draw a line to match each one with the
correct answer.

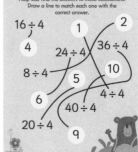

$16 \div 4$ — 4
$24 \div 4$ — 6
$36 \div 4$ — 9
$8 \div 4$ — 2
$4 \div 4$ — 1
$40 \div 4$ — 10
$20 \div 4$ — 5

Missing numbers　106

Write the missing numbers in the boxes
to complete these calculations.

$12 \div 3 = 4$

$32 \div 8 = 4$

$4 \div 1 = 4$

$40 \div 10 = 4$

$28 \div 7 = 4$

$20 \div 5 = 4$

Right or wrong?　107

Check if Tan-tan and Tig have answered these
calculations correctly. Put a ✔ or ✗ in the boxes.
Then, turn the page.

$28 \div 4 = 6$ ✗　$4 \div 4 = 1$ ✔

$40 \div 4 = 10$ ✔　$24 \div 4 = 6$ ✔

$16 \div 4 = 4$ ✔　$32 \div 4 = 7$ ✗

$36 \div 4 = 8$ ✗　$12 \div 4 = 4$ ✗

$20 \div 4 = 4$ ✗

$8 \div 4 = 2$ ✔

Correcting calculations 108

Complete the other side of this page. Then, copy
the calculations that are wrong into the blank boxes
below, writing the correct answers instead.

$28 \div 4 = 7$

$36 \div 4 = 9$

$20 \div 4 = 5$

$32 \div 4 = 8$

$12 \div 4 = 3$

Answers

Missing numbers 109

Write the missing numbers in the boxes to complete these calculations.

$8 \div 4 = 2$

$16 \div 4 = 4$

$4 \div 4 = 1$

$40 \div 4 = 10$

$20 \div 4 = 5$

$28 \div 4 = 7$

Number wheel 110

Help Cheeky complete the number wheel. Divide each number by 4 to fill in the blank spaces.

2 7

9 8 28 1

36 4

4 16 $\div 4$ 20 5

24 12

6 40 32 3

10 8

$\div 4$

Twenty-four
divided by four
is six

Sharing 111

Help Crock share out these 8 lemons equally onto 8 plates. Cross off each lemon as you draw it on a plate, then complete the calculation below.

$8 \div 8 = 1$ each

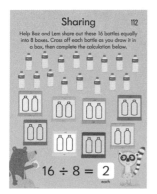

Sharing 112

Help Baz and Lem share out these 16 bottles equally into 8 boxes. Cross off each bottle as you draw it in a box, then complete the calculation below.

$16 \div 8 = 2$ each

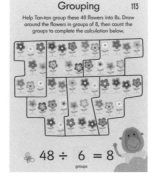

Grouping 113

Help Tan-tan group these 48 flowers into 8s. Draw around the flowers in groups of 8, then count the groups to complete the calculation below.

$48 \div 6 = 8$ groups

Grouping 114

Help Ant group these 64 flying bugs into 8s. Draw around the flying bugs in groups of 8, then count the groups to complete the calculation below.

$64 \div 8 = 8$ groups

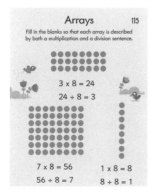

Arrays 115

Fill in the blanks so that each array is described by both a multiplication and a division sentence.

$3 \times 8 = 24$

$24 \div 8 = 3$

$7 \times 8 = 56$ $1 \times 8 = 8$

$56 \div 8 = 7$ $8 \div 8 = 1$

Fact family 116

A fact family is a set of three numbers that can be divided or multiplied together. Fill in the blank spaces below to show the two dividing and two multiplying calculations for this fact family.

48

$\div$ $\div$

6   8

$\times$

$48 \div 6 = 8$

$48 \div 8 = 6$

$6 \times 8 = 48$

$8 \times 6 = 48$

Fact family 117

Fill in the blank spaces below to show the two dividing and two multiplying calculations for this fact family.

56

$\div$ $\div$

7   8

$\times$

$56 \div 7 = 8$

$56 \div 8 = 7$

$7 \times 8 = 56$

$8 \times 7 = 56$

Answers

Domino dots 118

For each row, complete the calculation to show how many dots are on each domino.

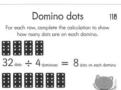

32 dots $\div 4$ dominoes $= 8$ dots on each domino

$48 \div 6 = 8$

$72 \div 9 = 8$

$24 \div 3 = 8$

Dividing by 8 119

These 24 animals need to be split into 8 groups to rehearse for a play. Complete the calculation to show how many animals will be in each group.

$24 \div 8 = 3$

Dividing by 8 120

Cheeky needs to divide 64 props into 8 piles. Complete the calculation below to show how many props will be in each pile.

$64 \div 8 = 8$

And how many in each pile if I divide 80 props into 8 piles?

$80 \div 8 = 10$

8 each 121

Baz is trying to collect 32 fireflies and put them into jars. Each jar has room for 8 fireflies. Complete the calculation to show many jars he will need to catch all the fireflies.

$32 \div 4 = 8$

8 each 122

The backpack on the table has space for 8 packed lunches. Complete the calculation to find out how many backpacks are needed for 56 packed lunches.

$56 \div 7 = 8$

And how many backpacks are needed for 72 packed lunches?

$72 \div 9 = 8$

Calculation match-up 123

Help Baz find the answers to these calculations. Draw a line to match each one with the correct answer.

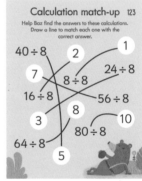

$40 \div 8$ 2   1

7   24 $\div 8$

$8 \div 8$

$16 \div 8$ $56 \div 8$

3   8

$80 \div 8$ 10

$64 \div 8$ 5

Missing numbers 124

Write the missing numbers in the boxes to complete these calculations.

$16 \div 2 = 8$

$48 \div 6 = 8$

$32 \div 4 = 8$

$72 \div 9 = 8$

$64 \div 8 = 8$

$24 \div 3 = 8$

Right or wrong? 125

Check if Tan-tan and Tig have answered these calculations correctly. Put a ✓ or ✗ in the boxes. Then, turn the page.

$48 \div 8 = 6$ ✓ $40 \div 8 = 7$ ✗

$32 \div 8 = 4$ ✓ $16 \div 8 = 2$ ✓

$56 \div 8 = 6$ ✗ $64 \div 8 = 8$ ✓

$8 \div 8 = 0$ ✗ $72 \div 8 = 10$ ✗

$80 \div 8 = 8$ ✗

$24 \div 8 = 3$ ✓

Correcting calculations 126

Complete the other side of this page. Then, copy the calculations that are wrong into the blank boxes below, writing the correct answers instead.

$56 \div 8 = 7$

$8 \div 8 = 1$

$80 \div 8 = 10$

$40 \div 8 = 5$

$72 \div 8 = 9$

$\div 8$